SIEGE

SIEGE

How General Washington Kicked the British Out of Boston

AND

Launched a Revolution

ROXANE ORGILL

SCHOLASTIC INC.

ISBN 978-1-338-33510-1

Published by Scholastic Inc., 557 Broadway, New York, NY 10012,
by arrangement with Candlewick Press. SCHOLASTIC and associated logos
are trademarks and/or registered trademarks of Scholastic Inc.

12 11 10 9 8 7 6 5 4 3 2 1 18 19 20 21 22 23

Printed in the U.S.A. 23

First Scholastic printing, September 2018

This book was typeset in Adobe Caslon.

Caleb Haskell, a fifer, later a private; kept a daily diary

Joseph Hodgkins, a lieutenant

Samuel Haws, a private who kept a journal

Henry Knox, a Boston bookseller who became a colonel under Washington

Sir William Howe, commander of the British forces, succeeding Thomas Gage, who was ordered back to England

Abigail Adams, wife of John Adams, who was a delegate to the Continental Congress

For my brothers,

Kip (1959–2012) and Rory Orgill

CONTENTS

Cast of Characters
(in order of appearance)

George Washington, "the General," commander in chief of the Continental Army

Joseph Reed, a Philadelphia lawyer, served as an aide-de-camp, or secretary, to Washington

The News from Boston, reporting on the state of affairs in Boston

Orders, daily instructions from Washington to his officers

Cyrus, a waiter or servant, a boy of the author's own devising

Martha Washington, wife of George Washington

William Lee, Washington's slave who travels with him

Introduction

The situation is this:

Seven hundred British regulars
Marched to Concord in April
Looking to steal weapons
Got a nasty surprise from some colonials
Who tailed them back to Boston.

Now it's June.

The British have command
Of the town and the harbor
All the islands and waterways.
Seven thousand regulars
Camped out on the Common
Closed the port
Shut down the shops
Blocked the thoroughfares with barricades.
Confusion
In every corner

One man can hardly greet another
Without fear of
Being seen
Or heard.

Across the river
In Cambridge
The rebel militia
Expands by the day
Fourteen thousand
(Or more)
From four colonies
Camped in the common pasture
And beyond
To Prospect Hill and
Roxbury village.
Men make tents
From sails
Build fortifications
On the heights

Just farmers
With picks and shovels
Firelocks from home
No artillery
No gunpowder
No experience.

There's more:

The Continental Congress
Thinks this lot can be turned
Into a professional army
Strong enough to force
The British out.
Delegates meet this very day
In Philadelphia
To choose a commander.

Make ready . . . present . . . fire!

Road from Concord
THE CENTER COMMANDED BY GENERAL WASHIN
THE COMMON
CAMBRIDGE
Main-Guard
Road from Watertown
Redoubt

SUMMER

1775

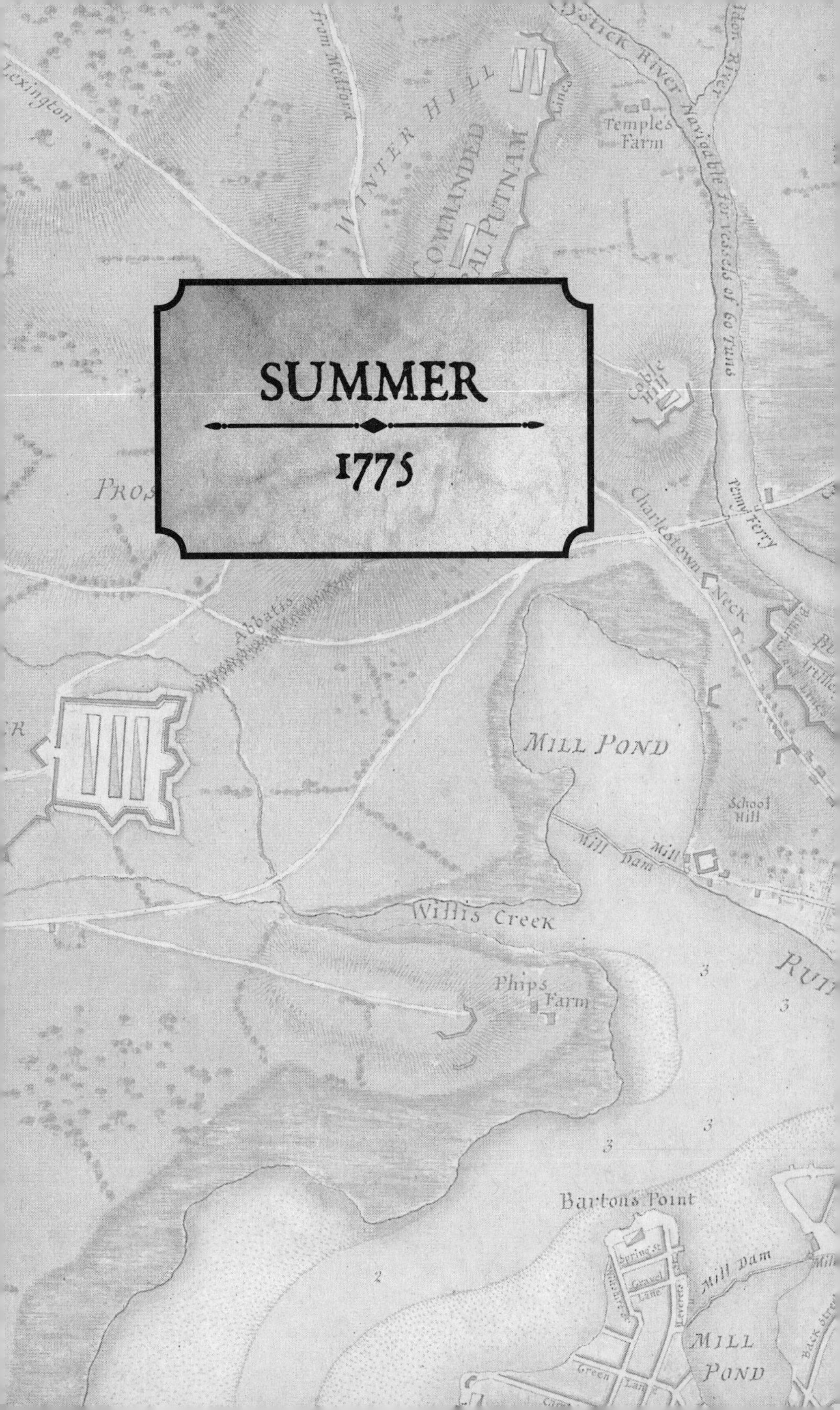

Lexington
From Medford
WINTER HILL
Lines
Temple's Farm
Navigable for Vessels of 60 Tuns
Cobble Hill
Penny Ferry
Charlestown Neck
Abbatis
MILL POND
School Hill
Mill Dam
Mill
Willis Creek
Phips Farm
Bartons Point
Spring St
Gravel Lane
Mill Dam
MILL POND
Green Lane

• George Washington •

He wore his uniform to the Continental Congress
Blue coat faced in buff, hat trimmed with silver lace.
Delegates began saluting him as "the General."
That's when he knew he'd been elected.
The vote in Congress was unanimous.
At midday dinner he was toasted
"To the Commander in Chief of the American Armies."

"I do not think myself equal to the command,"
He said, and would not take a salary, asked
His expenses to be paid—"that is all I desire."
Worried about leaving his wife, Martha, alone.

A crowd attended his departure
Congressmen in carriages
City officers on horseback
A company of light horse
Drummers and fifers
Beating and piping.

Some miles from town they bid farewell
Leaving him with two major generals
A friend named Reed and
William Lee, his slave from home.

He rode, a natural horseman, or changed
To the comfort of a four-wheeled carriage
But never in the whole journey, nine days
To Cambridge by way of New York,
Was he sufficiently at ease
To observe the countryside.

• What the General Saw •

tents
jumbled
this way and that
contrived
from any stuff
come to hand
cloth or scrap
wood or both
huts
constructed
of sticks or stones
or bricks
some thrown up
in haste some
forged with care
hardly one
resembling another
soldiers
in soiled breeches

shirts wanting
mending
shoes missing
stockings
worst of all
they'd been
relieving themselves
anywhere they pleased

• Joseph Reed •

Joseph Reed intended
to accompany
the General
as far as New York
then
turn around to attend
to his law business
wife and two children
their modest house
in Philadelphia.
Instead
Joseph Reed
found himself
going all the way
(there was much to discuss)
to headquarters.
When
the General looked at him
intently
with blue-gray eyes

asked him

to be his secretary

join his military family

he felt bound

by every tie of duty

to comply with

the request

said yes

then

wrote his beloved wife

he would not be home

for a while.

• George Washington •

General Washington
Astride a chestnut horse
Sixteen hands high
Rode with General Lee
Into Cambridge Common
It was the third of July
One-and-twenty
Fifers
One-and-twenty
Drummers
A-tooting and
A-pounding
Round and round
The parade.

Generals Washington
And Lee
Surveyed
The rebel lines

Eight miles in an arc

From Medford to Roxbury

Noted

Forts and citadels

A strong redoubt

Commanding the Mystic

Spied

The enemy still holding Charlestown

(Though in ruins

Since the battle of Bunker Hill)

The enemy

Almost near enough to converse.

General Washington

Noted all—

And wished for uniforms.

• George Washington •

At thirteen
He found some old instruments belonging to his father
A brass compass with two sights
A pointed staff
A chain one hundred links long—
Surveyor's tools.

He learned how to measure his brother's turnip patch
His mother's plantation, the neighbors' fields.

At sixteen
He crossed the Blue Ridge Mountains
Surveyed the property of Lord Fairfax
In the unsettled frontier
Was made surveyor for the county of Culpeper
A job that paid in cash or land.
He chose land,
Lots of land,
Which he measured.

At twenty-one
He walked from the Potomac to Lake Erie
To relay a message to a French commander
Measured his journey
Although no one asked him to
Noted directions and made a map.

At forty-three
Encamped without compass and chain
The General needed to know where he was
Location and boundaries
Bays and peninsulas, roads
And rivers, enemy forts
So he made a map.

The NEWS *from* BOSTON

A state of distress
Prevails
All business
Ended
All communication between town and country
Ceased
All provisions from farm to market
Stopped

The population has shrunk
By more than half
Patriots and loyalists alike
Gone to the mainland
Or to England
Leaving behind the poor
Who lack the means to flee
And the very rich
Like John Rowe
Who remains to watch over

House, garden plot, pastures

Lots and houses in other parts of town

His wharf and ships

Stores of salt and cloth

Even John Rowe

Neither a true patriot

Nor especially loyal to the king

Even John Rowe

Is disturbed

Spyglass in hand

Gaze fixed on the militia

Building fortifications atop the hills

Forming a great ring around the town

His town

Besieged

The NEWS *from* BOSTON

The British
Have sealed off
The Neck
A narrow causeway
Half a mile long
Linking town
With country
Ditches of some
Depth
Earthworks
Invincible
Double-guarded
To keep the rebels out
Unfortunately
Also effective
In depriving
Townspeople
Of meat and fuel
Vegetables, grains
Even gruel

: ORDERS :

Keep the men clean and neat.
Make sure they have straw to lie on.
See their arms are always in order,
Their victuals properly cooked.

Read the General Orders,
Daily orders from the General.
Lapses will be noticed,
Consequence severe.

Provide regiments with good drummers and fifers.
Execute properly the reveille upon the drum
Not half an hour before daylight but when
A sentry can see clearly one thousand yards.

Read the General Orders,
Daily orders from the General.
Lapses will be noticed,
Consequence severe.

Fill up old necessaries,
Dig new ones posthaste.
Stem the spread of disorders,
Fevers, the bloody flux.

Read the General Orders,
Daily orders from the General.
Lapses will be noticed,
Consequence severe.

Each soldier to furnish his own arms,
Two dollars to be paid to any
Who provides himself
With a good blanket.

Read the General Orders,
Daily orders from the General.
Lapses will be noticed,
Consequence severe.

• Cyrus •

Back home Father showed me how to load
a Brown Bess long-land flintlock.
There's not much to it, Cyrus,
he said.
Draw back the hammer at half cock
take a paper cartridge from the pouch
bite off the top, shake some powder
into the priming pan and close it
pour the rest into the barrel
take a lead ball from the pouch
stick the ball in the barrel
shove in the paper too
withdraw the ramrod
push the rod into the muzzle
tamp down the ball and powder
put the rammer back in its holder
cock the firelock
take aim
pull the trigger—
fire!

That's twelve steps
or more
a lot to remember
fingers slow
smoke in my eyes.
I got off one round
in the time it took Father
to fire three rounds
or four.
Not good enough for a soldier
he said.
That was then.

Now I serve
in the Continental establishment
as a waiter
to my father the captain.
I carry messages, run errands
anything he needs.
He puts me on guard duty

some nights
although it's not required
of a waiter
but I'm large for my age
which is eleven and
there is no place or danger
where I fear to go
and I can fire three rounds
or four.

• Martha Washington •

Waiting for a word since he departed,
Here she was, breaking the sealing wax—
A letter at last, penned by his own graceful hand.
He was to take command of the whole army
Raised for the defense of the American cause.
"Immediately," he wrote.
Perhaps he was riding this very day to Cambridge
Or was he already arrived among the soldiery?
His concern for her "uneasiness."
She must summon her "whole fortitude."
He would return to her in the fall.
But would he?
His affection "unalterable" by "time or distance."
Weeks and miles. Months.
In a large house in Virginia
Crammed with family visitors, servants, staff—
Martha, alone.

• George Washington •

As the Continental Army
Have unfortunately no uniforms
Inconveniences may arise
From not being able to distinguish
Captain from sergeant
Major from brigadier.
To avoid confusion
And being stopped
By the sentinels

The officer will pin a cockade
To his hat, a snip of ribbon folded
Like a rose, signaling with a glance
His rank.

Red or pink for a field officer
Yellow or buff for a captain
Green for a subaltern.
A badge of distinction

To be provided immediately.
The sergeant will sew a stripe of red
To the right shoulder, the corporal
An epaulette of green.

Officers in General Command
Must don a diagonal from shoulder
To hip, a ribbon wide in purple
For a major, pink for a brigadier

Green for the aides-de-camp
Who enter daily in a book
These General Orders
Issued by their commander.

For when he rides
Among the ranks at sunup
Noting trenches dug
Branches bound in bunches

For entrenchments
Muskets wiped and oiled,
When he surveys this ragtag lot
Fourteen thousand farmers
Fishermen, sailors
Coopers, chandlers
Shopkeepers, smiths
Their homespun shirts shot with holes
Shoes mired in mud to the buckle
He knows they will dig deeper, tie faster
Treat their old guns better
If they spy
In the dim light of a Cambridge dawn
Not a captain in a canary cockade
But their commander in chief
Bearing across his chest
Between coat and waistcoat
A broad riband of clearest blue.

• William Lee •

I came up from Virginia
With the General
Servant, huntsman
Slave to the General
His own "val de chamber"
He calls me Billy
Or Will
I go
Where he goes
All I do
I do for the General

• In the Morning •

William Lee
Sets out his corn cakes
With honey and butter
Hot tea without cream
He'll drink three cups
While Lee brushes dirt
From his clothes
Polishes his boots
To a gleam
Wipes clean the lens
On the short-range spyglass
Oils the rifle, sharpens
The flint, rolls the cartridges tight
"We're going hunting, Will"
He says and Lee combs his hair
Ties the queue with a ribbon
Saddles his horse, Nelson,
And a smaller mount for himself

They're off to round up deserters
Take dozing sentries by storm
Nab enlistees who poach
Potatoes from farmers
Seize rogue sutlers who dare
Sell rum to the troops
Hook soldiers who curse
Their superiors, and officers
Who beat their soldiers
Or steal their pay
Or draw more provisions
Than needed, then sell
The surplus
They'll land any man who
Wastes powder on a rabbit or
Just to make noise
(Nothing makes the General madder
Than blowing good powder)

Do they wish they were hunting
Foxes back in Virginia?
Coursing through Mount Vernon
Or one of the other four farms
Lee on his horse, Chinkling,
(Low but sturdy, like him)
Tearing through tangled wood
Keeping pace with the hounds
Sound the brass horn
To signal "fox is cornered"
Await the General's one true shot—

Probably.
Game sure is plentiful here in camp
But it ain't foxes

: ORDERS :

No playing at toss-up, pitch & hustle, or any games of
chance.
No selling spirits to soldiers except by appointed sutlers.
No fishing in Fresh-water Pond, near the smallpox
hospital.
No firing of guns to start a fire for cooking.
No running naked upon the bridge during bathing in
warm weather
While ladies are passing over.

Fine of fifteen shillings
Thirty lashes upon the bare back
Drummed out of the army
Dismissed, disgraced.

Read the General Orders,
Consequence severe.

• Caleb •

Pleasant weather.
We are daily employed in making
strong fortifications in different places.
A smart shower of rain.
Were something wet in our tents.
Alarmed in the afternoon,
proceeded to our post,
the alarm being false we returned again.
Our people at Roxbury went down on the Neck,
rushed upon the guard,
set fire to the guardhouse.
A hot firing on both sides.
Not one of our side hurt.
This morning heard a sermon from Isaiah 46:8.
All still.

The NEWS *from* BOSTON

They're battling dysentery
The "bloody flux"
Begun in camp
Among the soldiery
Spread to the citizens
It's in every corner of the town
Makes the bowels run
With blood, people double over
From pain, burn up with fever
Especially old people and
the youngest children
Funerals—three, four, five a day
General Gage has ceased
The pealing of church bells
They cast too melancholy a mood
They do not bring back the dead

The NEWS *from* BOSTON

A handbill circulates
Among the British Army rank and file
Under the very noses of the officers
Clever, it compares a soldier's life
On Prospect Hill, rebel fortified
With Bunker Hill, British occupied

Prospect Hill pay, seven dollars a month
    Bunker Hill, threepence a day
Fresh provisions on Prospect
    Rotten salt pork at Bunker
Prospect Hill, health
    Bunker Hill, the scurvy
Freedom, ease, and affluence on Prospect
    While Bunker serves up
    Slavery, beggary, and want

Serve the crown

Or exchange a red coat for homespun

And be a deserter—

Which will it be?

• One Long Night on the River •

"The Congress have allowed four dollars
to every deserter without his arms
and fourteen to those who desert with."

Private Thomas Machin
of the king's army
learned of the rebels' offer,
thought it over
while guarding a man-of-war
one long night on the river.
Waited until his mate was napping,
then grabbed the fellow's gun
so he could not fire for attention
if he should happen to wake up
and see Machin dipping oar into dark waters,
rowing away.

When rebel guards picked him up
Private Machin was toting

two of the Crown's firearms.
They took him to headquarters
for questioning.
The deserter did not hold back
but discussed freely his army's fortifications,
gave an account of killed and wounded
at Bunker Hill,
even explained how he'd invented
a new carriage for guns on a pivot.

The General, impressed,
ordered him to draw plans of enemy lines,
noting advanced lines and batteries,
forts and redoubts, ships mounting guns.
Paid him twenty-eight dollars,
made him second lieutenant
of the Continental artillery
and later, captain—
a rank

he would never have attained
in the king's army.

Years later
Captain Thomas Machin
sent a shell
into a small British vessel,
a direct hit to the magazine,
blowing crew to the sky,
the ship to bits—
to the great satisfaction
of his fellow officers.
He did not regret
not ever
his decision
one long night on the river.

From your loving husband until death, Joseph Hodgkins

If you could make me a shirt
I should be glad
I sent two pair stockings
They want a little mending

I should be glad
Pray send as soon as you can
They want a little mending
We have no woman here

Pray send as soon as you can
I fear I shall weary you
We have no woman here
I bought four yards of cloth

I fear I shall weary you
I sent two pair stockings
I bought four yards of cloth
If you could make me a shirt

: ORDERS :

No firing of guns for amusement, wasting precious
powder,
Inviting the ridicule of the enemy, disturbing the natural
rest of every soldier.

Read the General Orders,
Consequence severe.

• Samuel •

no news today
nothing of merit
happened
very cold a terrible wind
otherwise nothing
extraordinary that I know of
being Sabbath day
we had preaching
we passed muster
we had an alarm
this day
went to our post
for about an hour
but discovered nothing
no firing on either side
nothing strange nor comical
nothing worth a-mentioning
today

• George Washington •

He stood
All six foot two inches of him
To receive the news
From the brigadier general
On the situation of powder:
(May it please Your Excellency)
There remains in store
But thirty-six barrels
Not three hundred and three
As believed previously
Almost enough for each man
To fire nine rounds
But not a speck
Left to charge
A single
Cannon.

He stood

All six foot two inches

Knowing full well

The enemy had sixty rounds a man

He did not utter a word

For the next half hour.

• Joseph Reed •

He started early
worked late
writing letters
by candlelight
punishment and troops' pay
the next plan of attack
the ongoing lack of funds
(also artillery, blankets, and
especially gunpowder)
scratching on good paper
with a fine quill pen
to governors and officers
committees and Congress
early and late
by taper light.

He stole a moment
a letter to his wife:
"Events here are very uncertain;
don't think of me too much
or too little!"

• Smoke and Awe •

Ninety riflemen, tall muscle-bound lean,
walked from Virginia through forests over
mountains across swift wide rivers
four hundred and thirty-two miles.

Arrived in camp at Congress's request
dressed in long white shirts
and queer round black hats.
The General issued orders

for a show of marksmanship,
the target a row of seven-inch disks
nailed to stakes driven deep
at a considerable distance.

Drums beat—*charge!*
Fire at three hundred yards!
Balls whizzed, hit their mark—bull's-eye!
Another! Reload, fire on the run—again!

The crowd of militiamen, awed,
slack-jawed, fingered their firearms:
Brown Bess from home
smoothbore and slow, reliable.

Could never hit the center
of a saucer at three hundred yards
through smoke stinging eyes—
even to try, a waste of ball and powder.

: ORDERS :

No sleeping on post as sentinel.
No rambling from camp without written leave.
No destroying the fences of Watertown or stealing a
cheese.

Read the General Orders,
Consequence severe.

• Rolling Cannonball •

Due to a rumor
the British were going
to storm his lines
the General sent

twelve hundred rebels
to dig trenches,
throw up breastworks
on Ploughed Hill.

The British replied
with heavy cannon fire,
sent two floating batteries
and a man-of-war.

Blast! The rebels' nine-pounder
smashed a ball
into one battery,
sinking it.

Pow! The rebels' nine-pounder
shot a ball
at the other battery,
crippling it.

Both sides expected
full-out attack
at high tide
from noon to three.

Instead, the most awful silence.
One o'clock, two,
the tide turned and—
nothing.

Only cannon fire
from the king's endless arsenal,
noise aplenty
but little hurt.

The rebels took
Ploughed Hill,
held it fast
with a loss of just two balls

and four men:
Volunteer Simpson, his ankle
shattered; it gangrened, and he died.
Adjutant Mumford, his head blown off.

Two others slain by their own folly:
stopped a rolling cannonball
(hoping for a souvenir)
but they misjudged—

the ball was not yet spent.

The NEWS *from* BOSTON

Nightfall brings raids
From rebel guns
A regular frolic
To little effect

Here a ball might fall
In the middle of town
Cause no more damage
Than shattered glass

There a shell might soar
Linger in the air
Then explode
No harm done
A pretty sight

The racket
Has everyone
On edge

The NEWS *from* BOSTON

Not a potato, an apple
Loin of fresh meat
To be had
Everyone
Soldier and civilian
Alike
Is sick of
Gnawing on salt pork
Or salt fish
Spooning dried peas

All supplies
From the farms
Cut off
Ships bearing flour
Chickens, turnips
Hay, sheep, rum
From London
Seized
By rebel privateers

Before they dock
Or lost
In terrible storms

A minister
Fortunate enough
To locate
Two quarters of fresh mutton
Kept a portion for himself
Made a strong broth
From the rest
Enough to feed forty
Ailing prisoners and
Feeble poor
Meanwhile Admiral Graves
Of the king's navy
Receives pineapples
And turtles
From the West Indies
And does not share

• Caleb •

This afternoon had rain.
A man in a neighboring regiment was whipped
twenty stripes for striking an officer.
Pleasant weather.
Off duty today in order to pass muster.
A man rode the wooden horse for leaving
his post while on sentry.
Exceeding hot.
Some firing in the morning on both sides.
We expect the enemy to come out every day
and have for the week past.
All still.

• Punishments •

Sit on a sharp rail
hands tied behind the back
feet lashed with weights:
ride the wooden horse
fifteen minutes.

Receive on the bare back
nine lengths of whipcord
knotted to make one long span:
cat-o'-nine tails
thirty-nine lashes.

Hang by the arm from a tree branch
above a sharpened stake driven into the earth.
For relief he may step upon the point
and impale himself:
picket
seven minutes.

The job falls to the drummer
to lash his fellow soldiers,
to flay and suspend them.
Blood splatters his clothes.

Road from Lexington
PROSPECT HIL
Abbat
MANDED BY GENERAL WASHINGTON
LOWER
FORT
THE COMMON
CAMBRIDGE
Main-Guard
Lines
Redoubt
Redoubt

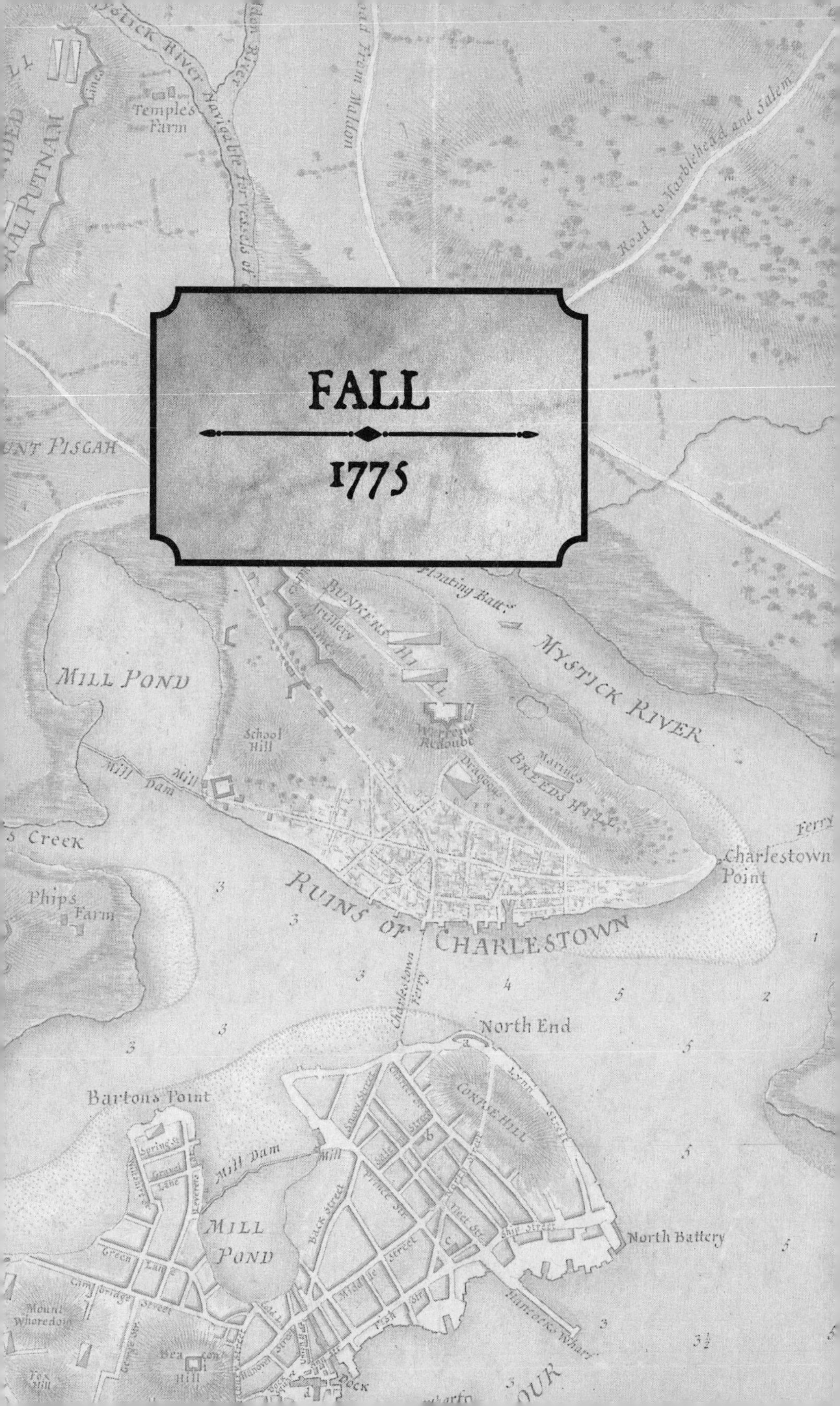
FALL
1775
Mystick River
Temple's Farm
Road to Marblehead and Salem
Mill Pond
Bunkers Hill
Artillery Lines
Floating Batts
Mystick River
School Hill
Warrens Redoubt
Dragoons
Marines
Breeds Hill
Mill Dam
Mill
Creek
Ferry
Charlestown Point
Phips Farm
Ruins of Charlestown
Charlestown Ferry
North End
Bartons Point
Copse Hill
Spring St
Gravel Lane
Mill Dam
Mill
Mill Pond
Prince Str
Back Street
Middle Street
Fleet Str
Ship Street
North Battery
Green Lane
Cambridge Street
Mount Whoredom
Beacon Hill
Fish Str
Hancocks Wharf
Dock

• Cyrus •

I go to Harvard Hall
to fetch the victuals—
"rations," they call it.

One pound fresh beef
or salt fish
one pound flour
or Indian meal
one pint milk
except in winter
one quart spruce beer
or cider
per man
per day.

I eat twice as much
as I did at home
Father says.
Food's plenty
but I'm always hungry.

A half-pint rice
three pints beans
or peas
per week
water not being safe
we drink beer
sweetened with molasses
nine gallons per company
one hundred men.

Candles three pounds
per company
per week
to light the way
to the guardhouse
where I think all night
about victuals.

• Henry Knox •

Bookseller by trade
Engineer by temperament

It's said he read
Every military book

In his store although
He never finished school

Tall like the General
But fuller in the middle

Bullfrog of a man
Surprisingly strong

Kept his left hand bound
In a white cloth

(Two fingers gone
In a shooting accident)

Built some breastworks
Like crescents on a hill

The General, impressed,
Invited him to dinner

Discussed the problem of
Powder lead mortars cannon

"For want of them
We cannot carry on any spirited operation"

Big guns especially
(We have but a dozen in all)

Those guns at Fort Ticonderoga—
They must be sent for

Three hundred miles distant
Across lakes and a wide river

Through impassable pinewoods
Rolling hills in winter

Henry Knox did not flinch
His mind already on sleds and oxen

Scows and canoes
Fathoms of three-inch rope

A last reminder from the General:
Don't forget flints for the muskets

• Henry Knox •

Henry wrote to Lucy
Keep your spirits dear girl

The General has ordered me
To go to Ticonderoga

About three weeks' journey
Do not be alarmed my Lucy

There will be no fighting
Only business

My only regret
Is to leave my love

The dearest object of my affections
Idol of my heart

I shall write at every opportunity
I am now in the greatest hurry

The batteries are waiting for me
Adieu for tonight

I think continually of you
Your ever affectionate husband HKnox

• How to Make Saltpeter •

Resolved . . . that persons within each of the colonies . . . shall work up such earth as is now fit for making saltpeter, and collect and place in beds or walls under sheds, all such earth and composition of materials as are suitable to produce saltpeter.

—The Continental Congress, November 10, 1775

Congress confronted
the shortage
of gunpowder
especially the lack
of saltpeter
an essential ingredient
to its manufacture
and asked citizens
to make saltpeter
at home.

Recipes appeared in newspapers.

Ingredients:
soil that has been permeated
        with animal dung and urine
water
ashes
straw

Dig in your stable or barn for soil.
Add water to soil, let sit for twenty-four hours.
Strain out liquid, then pour through ashes and straw.
Set to boil in an iron kettle.
Allow to dry for one day or more.
Turn kettle upside down.
Your saltpeter crystals will have formed
into a handsome cake.

• Sir William Howe •

General Howe hadn't eaten fresh meat in three weeks,
gazed through the spyglass at the cows grazing at
Lechmere's Point,
a peninsula encircled by marshes, almost an island at
high tide,
only one sentry for the whole point—why not steal a
herd?

Sent four hundred regulars rowing across the bay
under the wing of a man-of-war, a floating battery of
big guns, and a gang of twenty-four-pounders
positioned on Bunker Hill.
They seized the sentry asleep at his post and drove the
beasts to the boats
while a regiment of rebels waded unseen through the
marshes,
rifles held high and dry above their heads,
ran uphill without stopping, dodging the charge
of twenty-four-pounders kicking up clods of earth in
their faces,

dashed downhill to the shore,
got a shot at the regulars still loading balky cows
onto barges, stabbing one or two beeves just to be done
  with it,
then pulling on their oars in haste to be away.

Both sides claimed victory in the skirmish:
Rebels said they drove the enemy off Lechmere's hill
    and lost a couple of cows.
Regulars claimed they took the point under rebels' noses
    and made off with more than twenty head.

One thing we can be sure of:
General Howe had roast beef for his dinner.

From your loving husband until death,
Joseph Hodgkins

I want to see you very much
When I shall I cannot tell
Do not be troubled my dear
Write to me as often as you can

When I shall I cannot tell
But I will stay the winter
Write to me as often as you can
I hope I shall be preserved

But I will stay the winter
Do not be troubled my dear
I hope I shall be preserved
I want to see you very much

The NEWS *from* BOSTON

The smallpox
Is in every part
Of the town
First a headache
Chills, fever
Stomach cramps
Terrible dreams
Red spots
On the face
Spreading
To arms, chest
Back, and finally
Legs
Spots become
Pimples
Pustules
Oozing yellow
Crusting
Scabbing

The smell
Is awful
Skin feels
On fire
One in four
Will not recover
Survivors will have
Scars
Pockmarks
On their faces
Some may go blind

The NEWS *from* BOSTON

Poor people
Are being sent
Out of Boston
By the British
Shiploads
Of citizens
Disembark
Not far from
The rebel camp
Three hundred yesterday
One dead, two dying
Of the smallpox

Rumors fly—
"The British intend to spread the sickness!"
"Defeat the rebels with disease!"

Refugees are smoked
Like hams

Scrubbed clean

Clothing, blankets, too

Any persons

Showing signs of rash

Dispatched

To the pest-house

General Washington

Cannot afford

To take a chance

Smallpox

Could spread

Smallpox

Could ruin his army

• Prize •

Blast!

from the swivel gun

Blast!

from the carriage gun

HMS *Nancy*

of the king's navy

supply ship

bound for Boston—

captured!

Hauled to Cape Ann

unloaded—

what a prize!

Two thousand muskets

thirty tons of musket shot

one hundred thousand flints

thirty thousand round shot

for one- and twelve-pound cannons

grand prize: a thirteen-inch mortar.

Alas, no gunpowder.
Still,
great joy
in camp.

"Old Put"
(General Putnam)
mounted
the mortar
a bottle of rum
in his hand.
Crack!
Smashed the glass
christened the gun
the "Congress."
"Hip-hip huzzah!"

In London
a loss
much resented.

• Henry Knox •

Henry Knox arrived on horseback
With his younger brother William

Found an abundance
Of ordnance at Fort Ti

Brass coehorns, iron mortars
Field pieces in all sizes

Four- and six-pounders
Even a mammoth twenty-four

Three howitzers
With large bores

Guns in surprisingly good condition
Except for their carriages

Wood rotting since the last war
Easy enough to remove

And replace a frame
But how to move the battery

To the top of Lake George?
Henry Knox had it all figured out

A system of poles and ropes
Pulleys and oxcarts

To the one available vessel
A flat-bottomed gundaloe

Downriver to the Portage Road
Back onto the cart for a stretch

To the landing
It took three days

To get fifty-nine big guns
To the tip of the lake

Then load the lot onto
A scow, pirogue, and batteaux

Flat vessels and sturdy
With sails, a fair wind

Which died promptly away
Requiring much rowing

In icy waters
Six hours to Sabbath Day Point

Knox clambered ashore
A good fire, warm hut

Iroquois who shared their roast venison
But the scow tipped

In a fierce wind, took in water
Sank, broke all its ropes

William was aboard
The water was shallow

His brother was safe
Ditto the guns

More line had to be sent for
An inevitable delay

It pained Knox exceedingly
Knowing the need for haste

• Martha Washington •

He sent her an invitation:
Come visit him in Cambridge.
It will not be without inconvenience, he warned.
It may not be tolerable, with winter coming on.
She could feel the carriage tottering on rutted roads
Pitching on ferry boats in high tide
Even as she sat at her desk composing a short reply.
"Old Man" she called him;
He called her "Dear Patsy."

Packing leather trunks fitted with brass
Dresses tailored to her five-foot frame
Lace-trimmed caps, her garnet earrings
Sequined slippers, lots of knitting wool—
She must not forget anything.
She did not know how long.
Six hundred miles to Cambridge.
"Old Man" she called him;
He called her "Dear Patsy."

Departed mid-November;
She did not travel alone
But with an entourage:
Her son, his wife, five slaves
In white coats with red collars.
Along the way she was feted
By light-horse brigades and honor guards
As if she were "a very great somebody"
(She wrote to a friend)
Which pleased her no end.
In the evenings a maid shook the dust
From her dress.
"Old Man" she called him;
He called her "Dear Patsy."

It was almost mid-December;
An escort met the carriage.
Her eyes wide to the unfamiliarity of it all:
Soldiers filling snowy streets

Officers on horseback, sabers flashing.

The blast of cannon fire made her jump.

They stopped at a large yellow house

Crowded inside, aides scribbling

Servants on the run, visitors awaiting a word.

"Old Man"—he looked relieved at the sight of her,

"Dear Patsy."

• Henry Knox •

Henry Knox needed
Forty-two more sleds

One hundred twenty-four pairs
Draft horses

Five hundred fathoms
Three-inch rope

He needed snow
But first he needed ice

To glide across the Hudson River
Probably more than once

Depending how rough the terrain
On the other side

Ice thick enough to bear a cannon
Weighing five thousand pounds

Heavy as a thousand bricks
He needed drivers

He needed hatchets
To cut the rope

Should the gun fall through the ice
Instead there was a thaw

The inevitable delay
Pained Knox exceedingly

PROSPECT H
E CENTER COMMANDED BY GENERAL WASHINGTON
LOWER
FORT
THE COMMON
CAMBRIDGE
Main-guard
Watertown
Lines
Redoubt
Redoubt
CHARLES RIVER
BROOKLINE
Muddy River
ony Brook

WINTER
1775-1776
Charlestown Neck
Bunkers
Floating Batts
Causeway
Ferry
Mill Pond
Creek
Charlestown Point
North End
Bartons Point
Mill Dam
Mill Pond
North Battery
Hancocks Wharf
Long Wharf
Dock
The Harbour
South Battery
Windmill Point
Beacon Hill
Common
the Island
Boston Neck
Dorchester Flatts
6 Feet and Dry at Low water
4 Feet
Dorchester Hill
Dorchester Neck
Forster Hill

• Snowball •

Harvard College yard
under a blanket of white
muffled, a marvel
to Virginia riflemen
newly arrived
goggle-eyed.

Marblehead mariners
musket men
in search of mischief
spied the Virginians
poked fun at their moccasins
frock shirts with frills like a girl's.

Taunts returned with equal force
to the fishers' floppy trousers
cut short at the calf.

A snowball flew
another

a barrage.
Fifty men became
a thousand
biting, punching
gouging
a knockdown battle
sailor vs. huntsman
musket vs. rifle
north against south.

Up rode the General
leaped from his saddle
thrust the reins at Billy Lee
grabbed two riflemen
by the collar, roaring.
The musket men dispersed
riflemen quit the field
snow-scuffed and empty

except for Washington and

the pair of Virginians

chastised, contrite.

Court-martial not needed.

From your loving husband until death,
Joseph Hodgkins

It is a good deal sickly among us
The weather is very cold
We live in our tents yet
Captain Parker is ill of a fever

The weather is very cold
There was five buried Thursday
Captain Parker is ill of a fever
I am in good health at present

There was five buried Thursday
Our barracks are a-building
I am in good health at present
I rejoice to hear that you are all well

Our barracks are a-building
We live in our tents yet
I rejoice to hear that you are all well
It is a good deal sickly among us

• Joseph Reed •

No sooner was Joseph Reed
back home in Philadelphia
attending to his law business
than letters began arriving.

Long letters from the General

Complaining
the man who'd replaced Reed
had already left and his replacement
was no penman
"I feel the want of your ready pen greatly"

Imploring
his friend to consider coming back
"whilst you are disposed to continue
with my family I shall think myself
too fortunate"

Begging
him to tell Congress
of the army's considerable needs
"100,000 dollars will be but a flea bite
to our demands"

Sharing
glad tidings of a fortunate capture
the storeship *Nancy*
"we must be thankful for this instance of Divine favor"

Boasting
he'd taken possession of Cobble Hill
begun a bomb battery on Lechmere's Point
"the weather favored our operations"

Expecting
a capital blow by the British
any day
"General Howe is awaiting the favorable moment"

Brooding
over the lack of gunpowder
"nothing without it can be done"

Worrying
over Connecticut troops returning home
at the end of their terms
"our lines will be so weakened"

Agonizing
over troops from other colonies
following their Connecticut brothers
seized by "the same desire of retiring into a chimney
corner"

Wishing
he had never taken this job
that if he had foreseen the difficulty
"no consideration upon earth
should have induced me to accept this command."

Joseph Reed replied to every letter
did all tasks as requested
shared the burden from afar
knowing he was that rare man
to whom the General
(a person of great reserve)
could reveal
his true heart and mind.

• Retreat •

Soldiers
come to the end
of their enlistments—
a choice:
re-up or
go home.

Living in tents
a frigid winter
snowdrifts
blankets few
barracks expected
but not built
because there was
no wood.

Homesick
struck
by a strong desire

to retire
work the farm
tend the livestock
kiss the wife
meet the new babe.

The General's incentives
to reenlist:
furloughs
a month's pay
(forty shillings)
in advance
a dram of rum—
all declined.

Soldiers
come to the end
of their enlistments
sling firearms

across weary shoulders

walk away

to Connecticut

New Hampshire

Rhode Island

far corners

of Massachusetts—

home.

• What Did General Howe Know •

Of Washington's weaknesses?
His army's lack of gunpowder,
his difficulties with reenlistment.
Had spies brought word?
Had deserters with loose tongues
told all?

Most certainly.
Why else have spies?

• Martha Washington •

Homespun dress
Apron tied round her ample waist
The work in her lap
A needle, worsted wool thread
Darning egg, sock.
Table at headquarters
Set for tea
Not real tea—
Not since the "party"
In the harbor—
Huckleberry leaves
Brewed in a china pot.
Voices in the hall
"Mrs. Knox and Mrs. Greene."
In flounced fat Lucy
Bossy and loud
Pretty Caty fluttered
A sparkle in her hazel eyes
Generals' wives

Both young
One haughty
The other a belle but dim
Equally surprised.
Mrs. Washington
Dame of the South
Aristocrat
No fine embroidery
In hand
Mending
Her husband's stocking
Workbasket brimming
Pile of linen waiting
For sewing into shirts.
How lovely to see you,
Do sit down.

• George Washington •

The General's tearing his hair
Every day another fifty gone
Can't fight the redcoats
With twelve thousand men.

Confers with his war council:
Should Negroes be allowed
To enlist or excluded
From all service
Along with boys too young
And men too old to withstand
The toil of war?

The council argues
Disagrees on slave or free.
The army's no place
For a slave with a gun.
As for freemen, you're asking
For trouble if you allow even one.

They take a vote:
No Negroes.

The General's tearing his hair
Every day another hundred gone
Can't fight the redcoats
With ten thousand men.

He writes to Congress:
"I have presumed to depart
from the resolution."
He's letting the Negroes in.
Hoping Congress
Will not disapprove.

Comes the reply—
Resolved:
"Free Negroes who have served faithfully
May be reenlisted, but no others."

Tearing his hair
Building his army
Man by man
All over again.

• William Lee •

I'm standing in the corner
Waiting for an order
When I see it, the answer
In his eyes
Long before he says a word

He'll do what he needs to win
He'll let the Negroes in

• Bells •

Square-towered Christ Church
a barracks since June
but not this day
the first of 1776.
Troops ordered
to be quartered elsewhere
blankets rolled
knapsacks packed
canteens and cartridge boxes
cleared away
floors swept
at the lady's request.

Mrs. Washington
took a prominent pew
wore a cap to look taller
wished the other ladies
"the compliments of the season"
the General at her side

cocked hat removed
in accordance with custom
stacked with other men's hats at the door.

In the pulpit a colonel
offered as usual a prayer for the king
"Look down with mercy upon His Majesty
open his eyes and enlighten his understanding"
then went beyond—
"Bless the Continental Congress
be with thy servant the commander in chief
strengthen him that he may vanquish all his enemies."
A new kind of invocation
respecting king, Congress, *and* commander
a chorus of "amens."
In the square tower
bells rang
bells rang on New Year's Day.

• Grand Union Flag •

The General ordered
a schooner mast
seventy-six feet tall
erected on Prospect Hill,
a new flag
hoisted, unfurled
seen for miles.

In the top left corner
the white cross of Saint Andrew
signifying Scotland,
the red cross of Saint George
indicating England
crisscrossed, conjoined
on a blue ground,
abutted on two sides
by thirteen broad stripes
alternating red and white,
thirteen colonies prepared

to be loyal to the king
(also willing to resist if necessary).

A thirteen-gun salute:
"Make ready!
Present!
Fire!"
Huzzah!
Thirteen ear-splitting blasts
thirteen lusty cheers
thirteen clouds of smoke
merged in a gray fume
wafting toward the enemy
hovering over their ships
drifting down to the Common.
Huzzah!
To the commencement
of the new Continental Army
on the first day of the year.
Huzzah!

• A Word from King George •

The king broke his silence
on the present situation in America,
addressed both houses of Parliament
concerning "the rebellious war" being waged
for "the purpose of establishing an independent empire,"
noted "the fatal effects of the success of such a plan,"
called for "a speedy end to these disorders,"
pronounced Americans an "unhappy and deluded
multitude."

"His Majesty's most gracious speech"
(as the king called it himself)
took two months to reach America,
gave the General a good laugh
(Lord knows he could use one),
was read aloud to the troops
on the first of January,
every last word,
General's orders.

• George Washington •

The General's wish
When the temperature dipped:
A river of ice
Frosted over
Solid, arctic
Thick enough
To bear a battalion
Under cover of night
Frozen bays
Icebound coves
Rimy banks
All of Boston abed
Shivering
Unsuspecting.
Instead—
The temperature rose.

• Henry Knox •

The very last sled
To cross the Hudson

Crashed through the ice
Broke a hole fourteen feet wide

Cannon drowned
Night coming on

Next morning
The people of Albany

Turned out
Hands to work

Grappling with
Heavy ropes

Soaked
To the skin

It took all day
To raise the gun

Drag it to shore
Load onto a sturdy sled

Harness a fresh team
An inevitable delay

It pained Knox exceedingly
But would have been far worse

Had it not been
For the good people of Albany

The NEWS *from* BOSTON

At Old South Meeting House
Where Sam Adams once gave
The order to dump tea
Into the harbor
The British have dismantled the pulpit
Brought in dirt and gravel
By the hundreds of cartloads
Enough to cover the floor
They set up a grog shop
In the gallery—
Where slaves once sat
To hear the divine word
Officers will drink rum
While horses and riders
Of the Light Dragoons
Gallop round and round
A new riding ring

The NEWS *from* BOSTON

The British Army put on a play
A piece of mockery
"The Blockade of Boston"
Its target the rebels, of course
"The General" a rustic
In a floppy wig
Flourishing
A long and rusty sword
His "squire" a yokel
Clutching
An ancient musket

The play had just begun
A sergeant ran onto the stage
"The Yankees are attacking our works on Bunker's hill!"
The audience applauded
Enjoying the joke
Sergeant grew frantic
"Turn out, turn out!"

More applause
General Howe
The first to realize
This was no bit
Of tomfoolery
"Officers, to your alarm posts!"
A stampede
Soldiers tripping
Upturning chairs
Actors shedding
Costumes in flight
Calling for water
To wipe greasepaint
From their faces
One reached his post
Still wearing a petticoat

The call for alarm
Was real enough

In Charlestown

At the foot of Bunker

One hundred rebels

Had crossed the milldam

Burned eight houses

Captured five drunken soldiers

Stole a quantity of muskets

The enemy response

A smart flashing of musketry

Random and confused

The play

Will be rescheduled

• George Washington •

The General expected
Revenge—
Those houses burned
Men taken
Muskets lifted.

He urged upon his officers
The greatest vigilance and care
Especially at the outposts.

For reasons unknown
The British
Let this one go.

And the vengeance
The General expected—
Even longed for—
Never came.

• Henry Knox •

Tugging cannons up steep grades
Easing down sharp pitches

Using drag chains and poles
Henry Knox had his hands full

His mind ever on the waiting General
When they drew into Westfield

A crowd bigger than usual
Lined the main street

Clamored to examine the guns
Measure their length, circumference at the breech

Few had seen a cannon before
Let alone a caravan of fifty-nine

They spotted the twenty-four-pounder
Known as "The Old Sow"

Demanded a demonstration

Knox did not deny them

Had his men load a charge

And set her off

The bellow shook the ground

Resounded across the hills

The crowd silent

A long, solemn moment

Then cheers, the arrival of victuals

Strong cider, whiskey

An inevitable delay

Which did *not* pain Knox exceedingly

He put all haste aside and joined in the fun

• Joseph Reed •

In cold, dark January
came a cry of lamentation
such as Joseph Reed had not heard
from his friend the General.

My situation
the General wrote
"produces many an uneasy hour
when all around me
are wrapped in sleep."

No money in the treasury
the General wrote
no powder in the magazines
no firelocks for new enlistments.

I would have been happier
the General wrote
had I "taken my musket

upon my shoulder
and entered the ranks"
or better yet
"retired to the back country
and lived in a wigwam."

Strong sentiments
from a tired general
in deep despair.
He even got the date wrong
January 14, 1775
not '76
as if the year had not yet turned
as if his situation could be reversed
by the alteration of a digit.

• Samuel •

nothing today for news
one of the enemy deserted
and came to us
there was an attempt
to blow up a ship
but it failed
the morning began with firing
from the wicked enemy
at our guard
but did no hurt
nothing remarkable happened
today
there was a man killed
with a cannonball
we were all ordered
to lie upon our arms
at night
very cold
no news

that I know of

Lobsters fired upon

our guards

which was returned

the ball passed within

about four feet

of our barrack

nothing more remarkable

this day

• Henry Knox •

On to Framingham
By the grace of one last frost

A stopping place for the present
Cannons to be unloaded until needed

Henry Knox put spurs to hide
Sped the last ten miles to Cambridge

The General expecting him daily
Tardy by only three weeks

Knox recited the inventory
Forty-two cannons, sixteen mortars

Twenty-three boxes of lead
For melting into bullets and, yes, flints

Two barrels' full
He had not forgotten flints

The welcome was effusive
All lateness forgiven

The General had news for Henry
He was now a full colonel

Appointed by Congress
To command the artillery

Now that there *was* an artillery
He must ride to dearest Lucy

But the job was not yet done
Cannons all needed new carriages

His Fort Ti inventory was not enough
Must write to General Lee in New York:

Send the shells and shot stored at Turtle Bay
Those cannons held at Kings Bridge

The situation of powder as grim as ever
Without gunpowder to place in the barrel

And fill the quill for the touch hole
The cannon will not fire its shot

His journey will have been in vain

• Invitation •

"The General and Mrs. Washington
present their compliments
to Colonel Knox & Lady,
beg the favor of their company
at dinner Friday half after 2 o'clock."
Tomorrow!
Lucy Knox, thrilled.

• George Washington •

The perfect time
Before the earth thaws
Before spring
Brings reinforcements
To augment the king's army.

The right time
To draw out the enemy
Bombard the town
Launch an assault crossing by the Neck
First proceeding with a smart cannonade.

When Continental guns
Are sufficient in number at last.

A stroke well aimed could put an end to the war.

The army is not without deficiencies

The want of powder

lack of firearms

regiments as yet incomplete.

However

In the General's opinion

The opportune moment

Is

Now.

• Council of War •

They gathered, the major generals and brigadier generals
at the commander's request, to consider a matter of utmost importance:
the necessity of a bold attempt to destroy the British hold on the town.

Discussion was brief.

Advised, Your Excellency,
a request should be made for thirteen regiments of militia
to arrive at Cambridge and remain until 1st April.

Advised, Your Excellency,
an allowance of one dollar may be paid to recruits
who bring good firelocks from home.

Agreed, Your Excellency,

a vigorous attempt should be made to conquer the
troops at Boston—

as soon as practicable.

That is

when supplies are sufficient

regiments complete

when circumstances favor success

which is to say

not now.

• George Washington •

His hands tied
By his own generals!
His wishes
Thwarted again!

When would it ever be "practicable"
To pry loose the king's troops' hold on the town
To provoke the king's fleet to hoist its sails
Free the harbor, open the Neck?

Circumstances may never favor success
More than this very moment.

He must do everything in his power—
How far his efforts will reach
Only the favor of divine Providence
May determine.

From your loving husband till death, Joseph Hodgkins

I should be glad
If you could send me
A little coarse shoe thread
I have made four pair shoes

If you could send me
If you could spin some more
I have made four pair shoes
The officers all want boots

If you could spin some more
A little coarse shoe thread
The officers all want boots
I should be glad

• Joseph Reed •

Letter
after letter
arrived
from the General
the same request
more or less:
"Any hopes of your returning to my family?"
the General wrote
"Real necessity compels me to ask."

The need
more desperate than ever
for a good writer
a "methodical" man
a person who could think for him
who could execute orders, even
live with him in "unbounded confidence."
No one else came close to the mark
only Lieutenant Colonel Joseph Reed.

Joseph Reed considered.
His wife, Esther,
dear creature, so acquiescent
in his absence the last time.
His children, who must be removed
away from town to a safer place.
The Pennsylvania Assembly,
to which he'd just been elected—
what would become of his seat?

And yet—
he could think of no more just cause.

Joseph Reed, resolved
moved quickly.
He would resign
the assembly, find
a house for his family
accept the raise

(thirty-four more dollars per month)
rejoin the General
resume as secretary
(barring some event unforeseen)
in June.

• Gunpowder Geography •

Sought in Spain
Obtained from Martinique
Shipped from tiny Sint Eustatius
Milled in Philadelphia
Carted in open wagons from Providence
Unpacked from a brig off the Delaware Capes
A ton at a time
Barrel by barrel
Keg by powder keg
Bought or lent
Or confiscated
Enough for twenty-four rounds a man
Though still lacking for the cannons
But coming in
Slowly
From all corners

• Samuel •

nothing remarkable this day
nothing strange
the Lobsters came out almost to Cobble Hill
and took three cows
and killed them
and were fired upon
they were obliged
to leave their booty behind them
nothing remarkable happened
no news today

• George Washington •

I am preparing
To take post on Dorchester
Peninsula where the heights
Are closest to Boston.
We shall be able to command
A great part of the town
Almost the whole harbor.
Surely our attempt to fortify
Will draw the enemy out
Provided we can get
A sufficient supply of powder
Build redoubts in ground
Frozen eighteen inches deep
Move men and materials over land
Visible from Boston Neck
Within range of their guns.
I am preparing.

• Tools of War •

Artillery

Battery

Charge

Drumbeats

Entrenchment

Flints

Grapeshot

Horses

Ink

Jackknife

Kettle

Lead

Muskets

Nine-pounder

Oxen

Powder horn

Quill

Ration of Rum

Sleds

Tents

Uniforms

Vinegar to ward off the scurVy

Wagons

eXpedition

baYonets

huZZah!

• The General Wanted •

Fortifications built
on top of the twin hills at
Dorchester. Quickly.

Over dinner at headquarters
he told General Putnam
to consider the problem.

The ground being so hard frozen
digging trenches for the usual
earthworks was impractical.

Putnam, pondering, called
on General Heath; his eye fell
on a book, *The Field Engineer*.

He asked to borrow it but
Heath did not lend his books.
Putnam pleaded, pressed,

At last secured the volume.
Inside, a word, a French term
he had never seen before:

chandelier. A large timber frame
filled with long bundles of sticks
called fascines.

In an instant
a solution:
barricades.

Ready-made, movable.
Build them by the hundreds in camp,
cart them to the site,

Fortify with fascines.
Earthworks built *above* ground,
one atop each hill.

Approval granted.
Preparations to begin
immediately.

: ORDERS :

Clothes washed, arms cleaned
And in good firing order.
Guards properly posted and alert.
Ammunition and accoutrements complete.

Every man must expect to be drawn into action,
Ready in mind to engage in a noble cause.
If any shall presume to skulk or retreat
He will be shot down instantly.

There is no place for cowards in this army.

Read the General Orders,
Consequence severe.

• George Washington •

If the enemy will be so kind as to come out to us

Eighteen-pound cannons mounted
On the Heights will
Disrupt their approach.

Rows of trees felled and left
As barriers called abatis
Will slow their ascent.

Barrels filled with turf and rocks
Sent rolling downhill
Will cause considerable injuries.

• night of numbers •

7 p.m.
March 4
2,000 men
marched in silence
to Dorchester
carrying
3 days' provisions
led by a covering party of
800

360 ox teams
brought up the rear
carting chandeliers
gabions, fascines, and hay
also axes, spades
for redoubts to be built
on two hills
150 feet above the sea

from Lamb's Dam
Cobble Hill and Lechmere
a constant cannonade
144 balls and 13 shells
tremendous noise
little damage
but effective cover
for rebels erecting
defenses

3 a.m.
3,000 new arrivals
some as relief
for diggers and builders
others to occupy
the finished works
along with
5 companies of riflemen

keeping watch

in Cambridge river

45 batteaux

2 floating batteries

1 brilliant moon

The NEWS *from* BOSTON

The horror!
Spied from Boston's shore
At first light
Dorchester Heights
Fortified!
Seized
Overnight!

General Howe
In awe at the sight,
Was heard to say,
"The rebels have done more
In one night
Than my whole army
Could have done
In months"

Without delay

He sent

Five British regiments

To Long Wharf

Canteens filled

With rum and water

A day's provisions

Orders to sail

To Castle William

Opposite the Heights

Ready to embark

In flatboats

To drive the rebels

From their forts

Firelocks unloaded

Bayonets only

• George Washington •

A “rumpus”
The General called it
With glee
Writing to Joseph Reed.

The cannonade a continued roar
Twelve hours on both sides.
Our diversion worked its wonders.
I took possession without notice.

Two men killed
Five mortars burst.

Their loss unknown.
Not a creature
Has come out of Boston
Since.

• Cyrus •

His Excellency the General
came to us today
riding his tall horse
bearing words for the men
who took Dorchester Heights.
"Remember it is the fifth of March,
and avenge the death of your brethren!"
Who could forget
the bloody massacre
in King Street
six years previous
a cold night
snowball fight
five patriots gunned down
by British guards.
"The fifth of March!"
The General's words
passed from man to man

"The fifth of March!"
through every regiment
adding fuel to the fire
already burning in our hearts
until every last man was primed
for the fight of his life.

Then at nightfall
a terrible storm—
sudden, a wind like no other
a torrent so violent
British ships could not stir
their men could not disembark.
In the morning still more rain
and fierce.

Father fears the tempest
will quench the spark—

not in *our* hearts
but theirs.

I don't mean to be disrespectful
but I hope
he is wrong.
What if—
I dare not say—
what if the storm
puts off the fight?

• Abigail Adams •

Abigail Adams
could not sleep
for three nights
too agitated for rest
her heart kept pace
with the roar of twenty-four-pounders
the bursting of shells
the rattle of her windows
a steady cannonade
just ten miles from her bed

she wrote to her husband, John,
"I hear we got possession
of Dorchester Hill last night;
lost but one man"
she wanted to write more
all the particulars
but was too unnerved
by her own trembling hand

• Truce? Or Trick? •

A mysterious paper signed
by four officials from Boston
arrived at headquarters
accompanied by a white flag.

His Excellency General Howe
has decided to leave
with the British troops
under his command.

If the rebels do not molest them,
then Howe will not destroy the town.
If his troops are attacked,
entire destruction will result.

Washington considered,
conferred with his generals, replied.

Since the paper was not authentic

(it lacked a signature from Howe)

he would take no notice of it.

The General ordered

a battery built on Nook Hill.

Howe's ships still ringed the town.

Best to remain on guard.

The NEWS *from* BOSTON

All is hurry and confusion
The British break into
Stores and houses
Carry away
Anything
Steal rum and tea
Hogsheads of sugar
But not salt—
Salt they have aplenty
They throw it into the sea
So the people
Will have none

The NEWS *from* BOSTON

John Rowe unlocked his warehouse
Under orders from General Howe
Let in fifteen soldier's
Who set to plundering
Rowe could only watch in horror
Linens, checks, and woolens
Taken, gone
Two thousand two hundred
And sixty pounds' sterling worth
They gave him a receipt
He does not expect much to come from it

From your loving husband until death, Joseph Hodgkins

I do not know but we shall march soon
Which regiments will move is uncertain
The enemy seems to be flying before us
What the event will be God only knows

Which regiments will move is uncertain
The fatigues of marching will be great
What the event will be God only knows
There is so much confusion I cannot write

The fatigues of marching will be great
The enemy seems to be flying before us
There is so much confusion I cannot write
I do not know but we shall march soon

• Peering Through a Spyglass •

Ten-inch-long tube
mahogany ringed in brass
extended to its full length thirty-two and a half inches
one eye fixed unblinking to the little flared cup at the
    narrow end.
Every high hill
around Boston
had at least one
that morning
March the 17th.

The General
his council
captains, privates
wives and farmers
all staring.

Bays crammed
with boats full
to the gunwales
red coats and cocked hats

rowing toward
square-rigged
sailing ships
clambering aboard
load after tremendous load
until every soldier
had claimed a ship.
Anchors aweigh!
Nine o'clock
a flurry of sails
upon sails as far
as the eye could see
caught the breeze
billowed
propelled
a hundred vessels
south and east.

The enemy,
departed.

• Forward, March! •

From Dorchester to Charlestown
rebel drums beat to arms
line upon line, ready
to take possession.

But only those immune
from the smallpox
were permitted
entrance to town,

men who had suffered
the disease or
been inoculated
against it.

Colonel Learned
led five hundred men
with pockmarked faces
to Boston Neck,

so strongly fortified
it took two men
to unbar the gates
throw them open

only to encounter
a carpet of crow's feet
laid by the enemy,
four-pointed irons

strewn in the path,
one spike
jutting upward
from each device

designed to trip up
or pierce the foot
of a man or his horse,
to obstruct

the progress
of the opponent.
Only it didn't,
not much.

The five hundred
simply stepped
carefully
around the prongs.

Flags fluttered,
drums rattled in quick
time to the slow
forward march.

In the streets, joy.
Warrior greeted citizen,
friend. Congratulations!
Townsman welcomed

militiaman.
Congratulations!
Patriot embraced
patriot, speechless.

• What the British Army Left Behind •

Iron hoops, one hundred bundles

New ship, three hundred and fifty tons, scuttled

Vessel the *Washington,* armed, with ten swivels

Empty iron-bound casks, two hundred and eighty

Numbers of balls and shells

Twenty-four-pounders, nine

Oats and corn, six hundred bushels

Rugs and blankets, four thousand seven hundred

Your four-wheeled carriage, General Gage

• Abigail Adams •

what the Loyalists
and British officers
couldn't take
they burned
or broke
or hove
into the sea
or so I'm told

I believe it
from the jetsam
washed ashore
spindles
headboards
tables without legs
splintered drawers
carved backs
of Chippendale chairs

they're leaving the town intact
but nothing to sit upon

• George Washington •

Embarked

But not gone!

Incredibly

The enemy

Is anchored

In Nantasket Road

A waterway

Between the harbor

And the sea

Five miles distant

Hovering

Expecting

A fair wind

Or maybe

Fitting out

For a voyage.

To where?

It seems

The destination

Is Halifax

In Canada,

But temporary.

New York

May be

The true object.

The General

Has sent

His riflemen and

Five battalions

South

Dares not

Send more

Suspecting

The enemy

May yet intend

A vicious surprise

A parting shot

To preserve

Its honor.

The General waits.

He has strengthened

The guards.

: ORDERS :

Every officer and soldier
Will show the utmost alertness
On duty and off duty.

Officers will exert themselves
In sprucing up their men
To look soldierlike.

The whole army
Prepare to march
When commanded.

Read the General Orders,
Consequence severe.

RUINS OF CHARLESTO
Phips Farm
Charlestown Ferry
North End
Bartons Point
Mill Dam
Mill
MILL POND
Copps Hill
Lynn Street
Snow Street
Salem Street
Prince Str.
Back Street
Fleet Str.
Ship Street
Middle Street
Fish Str.
Hancocks Wharf
Green Lane
Cambridge Street
Mount Whoredom
Fox Hill
Beacon Hill
Royal Irish
Hanover Street
Dock
Long Wharf
THE HARBOUR
Beacon Street
King Str.
Queen Str.
Artillery
COMMON
Marines
Winter Str.
West Str.
Common Str.
Milk Str.
Summer Street
Long Lane
Battery March
Fort Hill
South Battery
the Island
Pond Str.
Frog Lane
Essex Street
Hollis Str.
Beech Str.
Orange Street
Newbury Street
Bennet Str.
Windmill Point
Intrenchment
Floating Battery
the Fortification
Boston Neck
Redoubt and Batteries
English Lines
DORCHESTER HILL
Dorchester Neck
FORSTER HILL
Circumvallation
George Tavern
BY GENERAL TH
Burying Ground
House

SPRING

1776

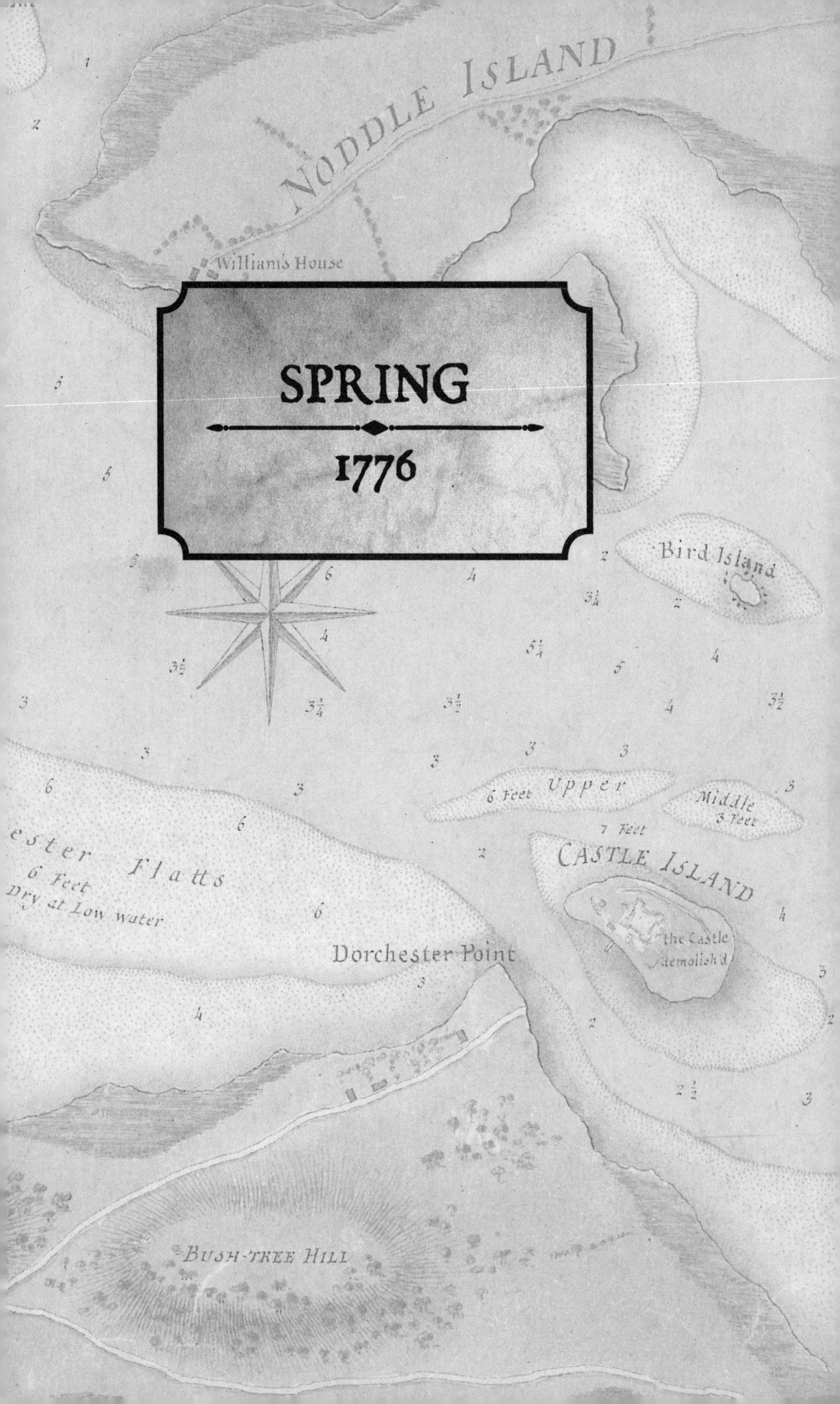
NODDLE ISLAND
William's House
Bird Island
Upper
6 Feet
Middle
3 Feet
7 Feet
CASTLE ISLAND
the Castle
demolish'd
ester Flatts
6 Feet
Dry at Low water
Dorchester Point
BUSH-TREE HILL

• Martha Washington •

Sent her carriage
To collect her friend Mercy
For a ride to Boston
To see for themselves
What the siege
Had wrought.

Windows smashed
Fences missing
Trees cut to stumps
Three hundred houses
Gone,
But they had been old.

A scene of wreck and ruin
Though less severe
Than anticipated.

: ORDERS :

Demolish as fast as possible
All fortifications on Boston Neck.
Level the earthworks,
Fill in the ditches.

Preserve the pickets and
Other useful materials.
Place them under the care of sentries
To be ready when called for.

Read the General Orders—
With pleasure, Your Excellency!

• George Washington •

For days
A fair wind
Blew
And yet
The British fleet
Remained
At anchor.

A puzzlement.
A delay
But why?

Then
One day
A fair wind
Blew
Anew
And
The fleet

Quit the coast
Altogether,
Bound
For Halifax.

The General
Still mystified
Took
A long
Breath.

• George Washington •

In the end
The enemy did not accept
The General's invitation.

His expectation
To force an engagement
His wish
A major battle
Or at the very least
To rake the redcoats with gunfire—
Dashed.

His disappointment
Acute.

From the President of the Congress to George Washington

Sir,

With every sentiment of esteem

the Congress has ordered

a medal of gold

to be struck in France and

presented to you.

Accept therefore

the thanks of the United Colonies

with every sentiment of esteem,

sir.

• Henry Knox •

Henry Knox got his orders
Assemble three hundred ox teams

Carriages for all the artillery
Transported from Ticonderoga

And all the covered wagons
Abandoned by the enemy

Fill the wagons with gunpowder
Load the musket balls, buckshot

Flints and fuses
In two-wheeled carts

Send the whole of it with all dispatch
Forward to New York

"Trusting in your zeal, diligence, and ability,
I remain confident of every exertion in your power"

The General wrote

Knox was confident, too

This expedition—

Ninety-one miles on actual roads

In April

By sea for the final leg—

Simple by comparison

To the previous trek

• William Lee •

I'm packing his trunks
Breeches, boots
Suits, shoes
With buckles
Knitted
Silk stockings
Beaver hat
Greatcoat
Waistcoats of wool
Shirts of linen
And cambric
With ruffles
Under-waistcoats
And drawers
All into trunks
Bound in leather
Trimmed in brass

We're going to New York
By way of Providence

Where the enemy

Still lurks

And the General

Fears an alarm

I go

Where the General goes

All I do

I do for him

• George Washington •

The General drew up a list

A light wagon with a secure cover
That might be locked on one side
A dozen and a half camp stools

What he required to set up camp

Plates and dishes
A folding table or two

On Long Island or another place
To be determined.

A pair of clever horses
A careful driver
And tents, three at least

The General looked around him
Perhaps for the last time

The room he had occupied
For nine months
As ever bustling with aides
Servants in and out
His usual place a round table
Seated in a Windsor chair
Warmed by the blaze
In a white marble fireplace
His gaze drawn to large windows
The view a wide meadow
Stretching all the way to the river.

In a day, or two at most
He would quit Cambridge
Travel with Martha and Billy
Depart with aides and generals
For New York.

He had vowed to Congress
"I shall exert myself
To the utmost to frustrate
The designs of the enemy."
But in truth
The General had little understanding
Of what the design would be—
An enemy enraged
A formidable navy, lately reinforced
A colony still loyal to the king.
He knew not
What to expect.
Only that once he got into a tent
On Long Island or someplace
He would not be at liberty
To leave it anytime soon.

Road from Concord
Road from Lexington
WINTER HILL
Temple's Farm
PROSPECT HILL
THE CENTER COMMANDED BY GENERAL WASHINGTON
LOWER FORT
MILL POND
Mill Dam
Willis Creek
Phips Farm
THE COMMON
CAMBRIDGE
Road from Watertown
Lines
Redoubt
Redoubt
Bartons Point
CHARLES RIVER
Floating Battery
the Island
Road from Watertown
BROOKLINE
Muddy River
Stony Brook
THE RIGHT COMMANDED BY GENERAL THOMAS
Pierpoint's Mill
Meeting House
ROXBURY
Lines
ROXBURY HILL

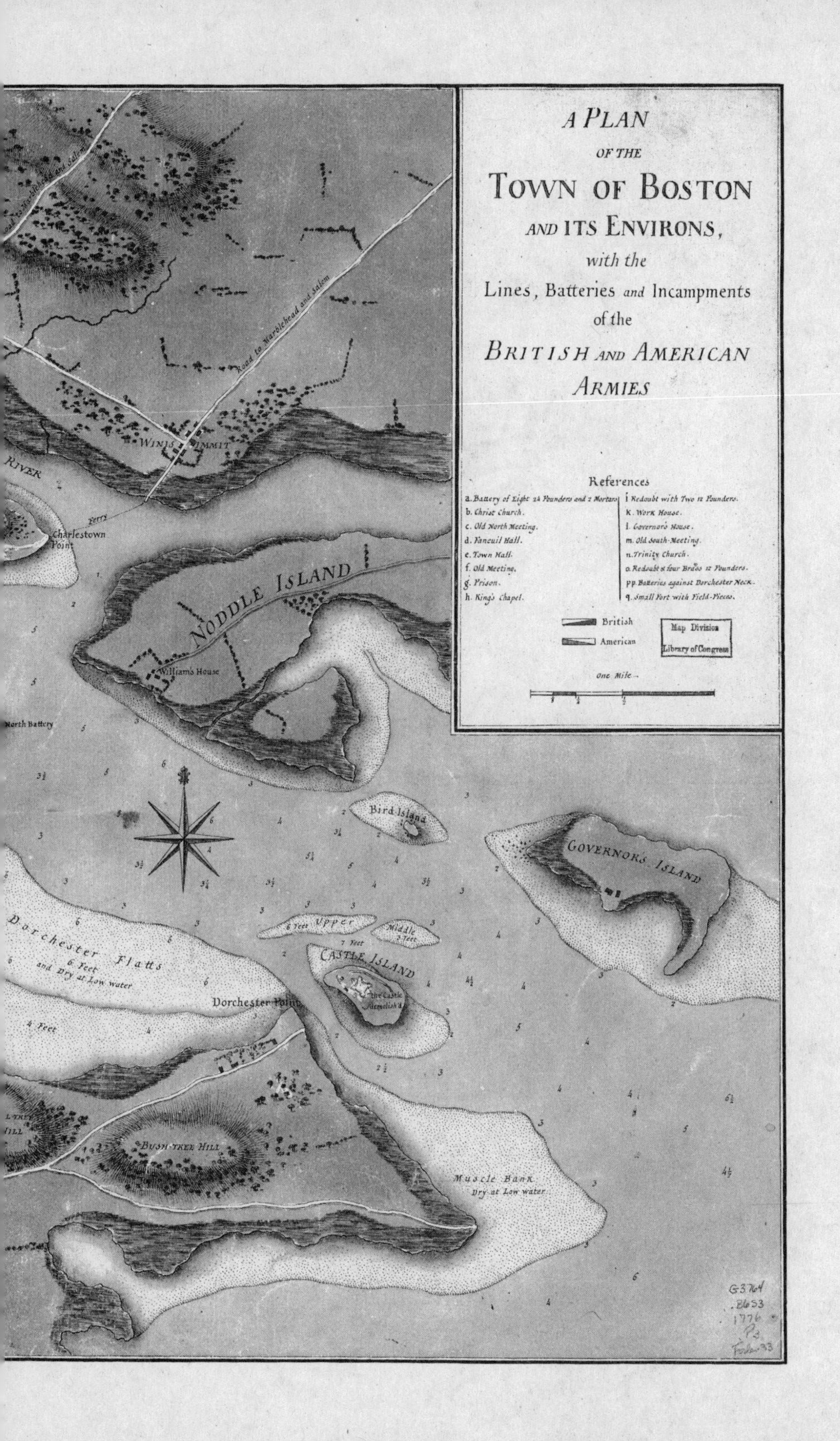
A PLAN
OF THE
TOWN OF BOSTON
AND ITS ENVIRONS,
with the
Lines, Batteries and Incampments
of the
BRITISH AND AMERICAN
ARMIES
References
a. Battery of Eight 24 Pounders and 2 Mortars
b. Christ Church.
c. Old North Meeting.
d. Faneuil Hall.
e. Town Hall.
f. Old Meeting.
g. Prison.
h. King's Chapel.
i Redoubt with Two 12 Pounders.
k. Work House.
l. Governor's House.
m. Old South-Meeting.
n. Trinity Church.
o. Redoubt & four Brass 12 Pounders.
pp. Batteries against Dorchester Neck.
q. Small Fort with Field-Pieces.
British
American
One Mile
Road to Marblehead and Salem
WINISIMMIT
RIVER
Ferry
Charlestown Point
NODDLE ISLAND
William's House
North Battery
Bird Island
GOVERNOR'S ISLAND
Upper
6 Feet
Middle
7 Feet
CASTLE ISLAND
the Castle demolish'd
Dorchester Flatts
6 Feet
and Dry at Low water
4 Feet
Dorchester Point
BUSH-TREE HILL
Muscle Bank
Dry at Low water

George Washington

Glossary

abatis: a fortification made from felled trees, with branches faced out toward the enemy; when the stakes are sharpened, an eighteenth-century form of barbed wire

artillery: big guns with a large bore (the hollow part inside the barrel), including cannons, mortars, and howitzers

battery: a place where cannons and other guns are mounted

beeves: plural of *beef;* used to refer to cattle

breastwork: a low temporary structure for defense; in the 1700s, breastworks were constructed of earth-filled baskets called gabions as well as bundles of sticks called fascines

breeches: men's trousers, short and fastened at the knee; Washington ordered his—along with all his clothes—from the best London tailors

cockade: a ribbon worn in a hat

coehorn: a type of mortar

Common: commonly owned land; a piece of land for public use, often for the grazing of livestock

crow's feet: four-pointed irons, four or six inches long, also known as caltrops, that were thrown in the path of the enemy to slow its advance; described by Sergeant Elisha Bostwick, of New Milford, Connecticut, as "horrid things for man or horse to step upon"

dysentery: an infection of the intestines resulting in severe diarrhea with blood

earthworks: earth built up in mounds, for defense

fascines: bundles of small branches or brushwood, tied securely in several places, measuring from two to ten feet long

firelock: musket

four-pounder (also one-, six-, etc., up to twenty-four-pounder): cannon distinguished by the weight of the ball

furlough: a leave of absence granted to a member of the armed services

gabion: a large basket, often made from willow branches, open at both ends; could be filled with earth and used to build fortifications

gundaloe: a flat-bottomed boat, also called a gondola

gunpowder: a substance made from saltpeter, sulfur, and charcoal that ignites easily and expands with amazing force; one of the strongest propellants known. Although the colonies managed to produce some gunpowder during the siege, most of the gunpowder they used was imported, mostly from the West Indies.

magazine: a place where arms, ammunition, and provisions are stored; a powder magazine stores large quantities of gunpowder

mortar: a short cannon with a large bore, used to lob hollow shells filled with gunpowder

musket: a gun with a long barrel and a smooth bore; the standard firearm of a Revolutionary War soldier, who could load and fire three shots a minute

naked: scantily dressed, wearing only underclothes (not used in the eighteenth century, as it is today, to mean wearing nothing)

necessary: outdoor toilet

the Neck: Boston Neck, a narrow strip of land connecting the peninsula of Boston with the mainland

picket: a peg or stake used as a holdfast for tent ropes and to hold fascines in place. Also used as a form of punishment, in which a person was made to stand barefooted on a picket for a length of time.

pirogue: a shallow boat with two masts, similar to the batteaux Knox used on Lake George

powder horn: a container for gunpowder fashioned

from an ox or cow horn and often engraved with designs and the soldier's name

queue: ponytail. Washington did not wear a wig, but he did sometimes apply powder, which turned his brown hair white. If powdered, Washington's queue was enclosed in a silk drawstring bag to protect his clothing.

quill: a pen made from the tail feather of a large bird (such as a goose). Can also refer to a tube made from the shaft of a goose feather and filled with gunpowder. When inserted into a cannon's vent hole and ignited, the quill lit the charge, which caused the gun to fire.

ration: usually a food allowance; includes, in this context, soap for washing both the body and underclothes (underwear)

rebels: used here to refer to soldiers and officers in the colonial militias and the Continental Army

redoubt: a fort relying on earthworks, usually temporary

regulars: used here to refer to British soldiers, because they were part of a regular, professional army. Also called redcoats or Lobsters because of the red coats that were part of their uniforms.

rifle: a gun with a long barrel and a bore scored with spiral grooves, which cause the bullet to spin, resulting in greater distance and accuracy than a musket. A rifle was also slower. It took the average rifleman up to a minute to load and fire one shot.

saltpeter: the mineral form of potassium nitrate, the major ingredient in gunpowder. Saltpeter produced in the American colonies in the first two years of the Revolutionary War went into the manufacture of some 115,000 pounds of gunpowder, but this was only one-sixth of the total gunpowder obtained, the rest having to be imported.

scow: a flat-bottomed boat similar to a gundaloe; both were employed on Lake George

scurvy: a disease caused by a lack of vitamin C and resulting in swollen, bleeding gums. To ward off scurvy, rations included cider and vinegar, since fresh vegetables and fruit were rare.

smallpox: a deadly and highly contagious disease that began with a high fever, followed by the formation of blisters all over the skin. There was no cure, and although inoculation was possible, there was much fear of it. Washington had survived the disease as a young man and was thus immune, though keenly aware of the danger to his army.

spyglass: a small handheld telescope

sutlers: people who followed an army and sold goods to the soldiers

victuals (pronounced "vittles"): supplies of food

waistcoat: a man's vest, worn over a shirt

wooden horse: a triangular wooden device which the soldier straddled with legs dangling (and sometimes weighted) as a punishment

works: fortifications made around a place for its security

HENRY KNOX

Source Notes

p. 3: "To the Commander in Chief of the American Armies": Quoted in Chernow, p. 187.

p. 3: "I do not think myself equal to the command" and "that is all I desire": George Washington, Address to the Continental Congress, June 16, 1775, *Founders Online.*

p. 21: "Immediately," "uneasiness," and "whole fortitude": George Washington to Martha Washington, June 18, 1775, *Founders Online.*

p. 21: "unalterable," and "time or distance": George Washington to Martha Washington, June 23, 1775, *Founders Online.*

p. 25: William Lee: George Washington Parke Custis, Martha Washington's grandson, referred in his memoirs to Lee as a "fearless huntsman" and "favorite body servant of the chief." He was also enslaved, and like most other enslaved people, was likely illiterate and left no account of his life. The most thorough description of William Lee's abilities, character, and status in Washington's household is in Hirschfeld, pp. 96–112. Observations by Washington and others indicate that he was present with the General throughout the war, including on the battlefield.

In my portrayal, I have tried to treat Lee as a full and talented person while also keeping in mind the troubling fact of his enslavement. Lee was Washington's property, *and* he made a significant contribution to the rebels' ultimate victory over the British, serving Washington in myriad and specific ways. When the General freed his slaves upon his death, he gave Lee an annuity for life for "his faithful services during the Revolutionary War" (George Washington's Last Will and Testament, July 9, 1799, www.mountvernon.org).

p. 34: "One Long Night on the River": "The Congress have allowed . . . desert with": George Washington to William Livingston, July 8, 1775, *Founders Online*. J. L. Bell, "The Early Life of Thomas Machin," "The Holes in Thomas Machin's Biography," and "The Truth about Thomas Machin," *Boston 1775* (blog), March 8–10, 2013, http://boston1775.net.

p. 43: "Events here . . . too much or too little!": Joseph Reed to Esther Reed, July 26, 1775, in Reed, p. 116.

p. 47: "Rolling Cannonball": Charles C. Smith and Samuel A. Green, "May Meeting 1894: Diary of Jabez Fitch, Jr.," in *Proceedings of the Massachusetts Historical Society,* Second Series, vol. 9, 1894–1895, pp. 40–95, http://www.jstor.org/stable/25079765.

p. 54: "Punishments": General Orders, July 10 and December 2, 1775. *Founders Online.* James Thacher, *A Military Journal During the American Revolutionary War, from 1775 to 1783* (Boston: Richardson and Lord, 1823), pp. 222–224.

p. 62: "For want of them we cannot carry on any spirited operation": George Washington to Philip Schuyler, November 16, 1775, *Founders Online.*

p. 66: "How to Make Saltpeter": *Journals of the Continental Congress 1774–1789,* June 10, 1775, and July 28, 1775.

p. 66: "Resolved . . . suitable to produce saltpeter":

Journals of the Continental Congress 1774–1789, November 10, 1775.

p. 82: "a very great somebody": Martha Washington to Elizabeth Ramsay, December 30, 1775, *Martha Washington: A Life,* http://marthawashington.us/items/show/85.

p. 89: "Snowball": This incident is described by Israel Trask in Dann, pp. 408–409.

pp. 93–96: "I feel the want of your ready pen greatly," "100,000 dollars will be but a flea bite to our demands," "General Howe is awaiting the favorable moment," "nothing without it can be done," "our lines will be so weakened," and "no consideration upon earth should have induced me to accept this command": George Washington to Joseph Reed, November 28, 1775, *Founders Online.*

p. 93: "whilst you are disposed . . . think myself too fortunate": George Washington to Joseph Reed, November 20, 1775, *Founders Online.*

p. 94: "we must be thankful for this instance of Divine favor" and "the weather favored our operations": George Washington to Joseph Reed, November 30, 1775, *Founders Online.*

p. 95: "the same desire of retiring into a chimney corner": George Washington to Joseph Reed, January 4, 1776, *Founders Online.*

p. 104: "I have presumed to depart from the resolution": George Washington to John Hancock, President of Congress, December 31, 1775, *Founders Online.*

p. 104: "Free Negroes . . . may be reenlisted, but no others": *Journals of the Continental Congress 1774–1789,* January 16, 1776.

p. 108: "Look down with mercy . . . his understanding" and "Bless the Continental Congress . . . all his enemies": Palfrey, John. "Life of William Palfrey," *Library of Congress American Biography,* Harper, 1845, 17:405–6.

p. 109: Design of the Grand Union Flag: https://publications.usa.gov/epublications/ourflag/history3.htm.

p. 111: "the rebellious war," "the purpose of establishing an independent empire," "the fatal effects of the success of such a plan," "a speedy end to these disorders," "unhappy and deluded multitude," and "His Majesty's most gracious speech": King George III, Address to Parliament, October 27, 1775, Library of Congress, http://hdl.loc.gov/loc.rbc/rbpe.10803800.

p. 111: The description of Washington's reaction to the king's missive is from George Washington to Joseph Reed, January 4, 1776, *Founders Online*.

pp. 122–123: "produces many an uneasy . . . wrapped in sleep," "taken my musket . . . entered the ranks," and "retired to the back country . . . in a wigwam": George Washington to Joseph Reed, January 14, 1776, *Founders Online*.

p. 129: Invitation: George Washington to Lucy Knox and Henry Knox, February 1, 1776, Gilder Lehrman Institute of American History, GLC02437.00247.

p. 136: "Any hopes of your returning to my family?" "Real necessity compels me to ask," "methodical," and "unbounded confidence": George Washington to Joseph Reed, January 23, 1776, *Founders Online.*

p. 149: "night of numbers": George Washington to John Hancock, March 7, 1776, *Founders Online.*

p. 152: "The rebels have done more . . . could have done in months": Quoted in French, p. 660.

p. 154: "rumpus": George Washington to Joseph Reed, March 7, 1776, *Founders Online.*

p. 155: "Remember it is the fifth of March . . . death of your brethren!": Quoted in William Gordon, *The History of the Rise, Progress and Establishment of the Independence of the United States of America,* vol. 2 (New York: Samuel Campbell/John Woods, 1801), p. 28, https://archive.org/details/historyofrise02gord.

p. 158: "I hear we got possession of Dorchester Hill . . . lost but one man": Abigail Adams to John Adams, March 2–10, 1776, in Adams, pp. 98–103.

p. 164: "Peering Through a Spyglass": *Boston, Its Environs and Harbour, with the Rebels Works Raised against That Town in 1775,* Library of Congress Geography and Map Division, https://lccn.loc.gov/gm71000623. One of Washington's spyglasses can be seen at Mount Vernon: http://www.mountvernon.org/preservation/.

p. 170: "What the British Army Left Behind": Enclosure: Inventory of British Stores Left in Boston, March 20, 1776, and Enclosure: Return of British Ordnance Stores Left in Boston, March 22, 1776, *Founders Online.*

p. 184: "From the President of the Congress to George Washington": John Hancock to George Washington, April 2, 1776, *Founders Online.* The Washington Before Boston Medal was the first Congressional gold medal; it features a bust of Washington on one side, and on the other, the commander and his officers on horse-back, observing the evacuation. http://www.coins.nd.edu/WashToken/WashTokenText/1790.html#Baker-48H.

p. 185: "Trusting in your zeal . . . every exertion

in your power": George Washington, Orders and Instructions for Colonel Henry Knox, April 3, 1776, *Founders Online.*

p. 191: "I shall exert myself . . . designs of the enemy": George Washington to John Hancock, April 1, 1776, *Founders Online.*

p. 196: "horrid things for . . . step upon": Quoted in William S. Powell, "A Connecticut Soldier Under Washington: Elisha Bostwick's Memoirs of the First Years of the Revolution," *William and Mary Quarterly* 6, no. 1 (1949): 100, http://www.jstor.org/stable/1921863.

General Howe

Bibliography

The poems in this book are nonfiction in that they are based on actual sources. But they are *poems* and as such are the result of both study *and* imagination. A single poem may have a dozen sources, including many primary ones, such as maps, letters, diaries, objects, and military orderly books. A list of significant sources follows.

Adams, John. Margaret A. Hogan and C. James Taylor, eds. *My Dearest Friend: Letters of Abigail and John Adams.* Cambridge, MA: Belknap Press, 2010.

Barker, John. *The British in Boston: Being the Diary of Lieutenant John Barker of the King's Own Regiment from November 15, 1774, to May 31, 1776.* Cambridge, MA: Harvard University Press, 1924. https://catalog.hathitrust.org/Record/007918059.

Bell, J. L. *Boston 1775.* http://boston1775.net. This daily blog is fascinating reading.

———. *George Washington's Headquarters and Home, Cambridge, Massachusetts: Historic Resource Study.* Washington, DC: U.S. Department of the Interior /National Park Service: 2012. The most complete account of the siege.

Brady, Patricia. *Martha Washington: An American Life.* New York: Viking, 2005.

Callahan, North. *Henry Knox: General Washington's General.* New York: Rinehart, 1958.

Chernow, Ron. *Washington: A Life.* New York: Penguin, 2010.

Dann, John C., ed. *The Revolution Remembered: Eyewitness Accounts of the War of Independence.* Chicago: University of Chicago Press, 1980.

Fenn, Elizabeth A. *Pox Americana: The Great Smallpox Epidemic of 1775–82.* New York: Hill and Wang, 2001.

Fields, Joseph E. *Worthy Partner: The Papers of Martha Washington.* Westport, CT: Greenwood, 1994.

Founders Online, National Archives. https://founders.archives.gov/. Washington's complete correspondence is available online; I found this site to be the most useful. His letters can be revealing: for instance, he boasted generally of having achieved victory in Boston, but to his brother he unmasked his "disappointment" in the outcome of the siege (George Washington to John Augustine Washington, March 31, 1776, *Founders Online*). He was sure, on the other hand, of victory in the skirmish at Lechmere's Point (George Washington to John Hancock, November 11, 1775, *Founders Online*).

Only three of Washington's letters to Martha survive; upon his death, she burned what she thought were all of his letters, but three more were found later. Of these, only two, from June 1775, are of interest, and both are available at this site.

The General Orders that Washington issued daily throughout the siege are also available at this site. They reveal in fascinating detail the frustrations he experienced in building America's first army. Of particular interest: General Orders, July 11 and August 22, 1775, on discipline; General Orders, July 20 and 23, 1775, on his preoccupation with uniforms; and General Orders, July 8, 1775, on the army's rations.

French, Allen. *The Siege of Boston.* New York: Macmillan, 1911.

Frothingham, Richard. *History of the Siege of Boston and of the Battles of Lexington, Concord, and Bunker Hill.* Boston: Little and Brown, 1849.

Gilder Lehrman Institute of American History, New York. www.gilderlehrman.org. Of particular interest in this collection are the love letters between Lucy and Henry Knox, which begin on July 7, 1775, GLC02437.00197. Henry Knox to Lucy Knox, November 16, 1775, GLC02437.00209. Also of interest: Henry Knox to George Washington, December 12, 1775, GLC02437.00222.

Greenwood, John. *The Revolutionary Services of John Greenwood of Boston and New York, 1775–1783.* New York: De Vinne, 1922. This source was useful in my creation of the composite character Cyrus.

Haskell, Caleb. Lothrop Withington, ed. *Caleb Haskell's Diary, May 5, 1775–May 30, 1776: A Revolutionary Soldier's Record Before Boston and with*

Arnold's Quebec Expedition. Newburyport, MA: William H. Huse, 1881. https://archive.org/details/calebhaskellsdia00hask.

Haws, Samuel. "A Journal for 1775." In *The Military Journals of Two Private Soldiers 1758–1775*. Poughkeepsie, NY: Abraham Tomlinson, 1855. https://archive.org/details/militaryjournals00tomliala.

Hirschfeld, Fritz. "Billy Lee," Chapter 9 in *George Washington and Slavery: A Documentary Portrayal*. Columbia: University of Missouri Press, 1997.

Journals of the Continental Congress, 1774–1789. Vols. 2–4. Washington, DC: Government Printing Office, 1905–1906. http://memory.loc.gov/ammem/.

Knox, Henry, Papers. Massachusetts Historical Society, Boston. Of particular interest: Henry Knox Diary, November 20, 1775–January 13, 1776, the diary he kept during the Ticonderoga expedition. http://www.masshist.org/revolution/doc-viewer.php?old=1&mode=nav&item_id=501.

Manual of Instruction for the Safe Use of Reproduction Flintlock Rifles and Muskets in Interpretive Demonstrations. National Park Service. https://www.nps.gov/stri/upload/18thCMusketManual2010-01-21.pdf.

Martha Washington: A Life. George Washington's Mount Vernon and the Roy Rosenzweig Center for History and New Media. http://marthawashington.us. A wealthy widow with two children when she married Washington, Martha spent the winter of 1775 to 1776 in camp, which became her practice every winter of the war. This site includes her description of the Cambridge camp in a letter: Martha Washington to Elizabeth Ramsay, December 30, 1775. http://marthawashington.us/items/.

Metz, Elizabeth Ryan. "Israel Trask Sees Washington for the First Time." Chapter 2 in *I Was a Teenager in the American Revolution: 21 Young Patriots and Two Tories Tell Their Stories.* Jefferson, NC: McFarland, 2006. I drew on this chapter for the character Cyrus.

Moore, Frank, ed. *Diary of the American Revolution: From Newspapers and Original Documents.* Vol. 1.

New York: Charles Scribner, 1860. The contemporaneous account of the fight at Lechmere's Point, pp. 166–169, was particularly useful.

Murray, Anne Wood. "George Washington's Apparel." *Antiques* 118 (July 1980), 121–125. The General was fastidious about clothes and, unusually for men of his time, he wore underwear, known as "small clothes"—cared for by William, of course.

Newell, Timothy. *A Journal Kept During the Time Boston Was Shut Up in 1775–6*. In *Collections of the Massachusetts Historical Society*, vol. 1. Boston, MA: Massachusetts Historical Society, 1852. This source was useful for knowing how the British set up a riding ring in Old South Meeting House.

Puls, Mark. *Henry Knox: Visionary General of the American Revolution*. New York: Palgrave Macmillan, 2008.

Reed, William B. *The Life and Military Correspondence of Joseph Reed*. Vol. 1. Philadelphia: Lindsay and Blakiston, 1847. Reed went home to his law practice in Philadelphia in October 1775 but continued to advise and assist the General via letters. Washington was more frank and revealing to Reed than to any other correspondent during this period.

Risch, Erna. *Supplying Washington's Army.* Washington, DC: U.S. Army Center of Military History, 1986. A comprehensive look at the supply problems Washington faced, from flour to flints.

Rowe, John. *The Diary of John Rowe, a Boston Merchant, 1764–1779*. Cambridge, MA: John Wilson, 1895.

Stevens, Benjamin Franklin, ed. *General Sir William Howe's Orderly Book: At Charleston, Boston and Halifax, June 17 1775 to 1776 26 May*. London: Benjamin Franklin Stevens, 1890.

Thompson, Mary V. *Statements Regarding the Physical Appearance and Personal Characteristics of George Washington (1732–1799)*. Mount Vernon, VA: Mount Vernon Ladies Association, 2005–2014.

Wade, Herbert T., and Robert A. Lively. *This Glorious Cause: The Adventures of Two Company Officers in Washington's Army.* Princeton, NJ: Princeton

University Press, 1958. This source includes the wartime corespondence between Joseph Hodgkins and his wife, Sarah. He typically signed his letters, "your loving husband till death."

In addition, visits to these historical sites provided context and a vivid sense of place:

Fort Ticonderoga, Ticonderoga, NY.

Longfellow House–George Washington's Headquarters, Cambridge, MA.

Mount Vernon, George and Martha Washington's home and farm, Mount Vernon, VA.

Acknowledgments

I would like to acknowledge the following: J. L. Bell, blogger extraordinaire (*Boston 1775*), and Don N. Hagist, editor of the *Journal of the American Revolution*; the Wertheim Room of the New York Public Library; and my husband, Conrad Bahlke, for taking me to my first Revolutionary War battlefield (Monmouth Battlefield, in New Jersey), thereby igniting a spark, which in time became this book.

ROXANE ORGILL is an award-winning writer on music and the author of several books for children, including the *Boston Globe–Horn Book* Award winner *Jazz Day: The Making of a Famous Photograph,* illustrated by Francis Vallejo; *Skit-Scat Raggedy Cat: Ella Fitzgerald,* illustrated by Sean Qualls; and *Footwork: The Story of Fred and Adele Astaire,* illustrated by Stéphane Jorisch. Roxane Orgill lives in Dobbs Ferry, New York.